SPEC CARTOON BOOK 2001

Edited by
Michael Heath

P
PROFILE BOOKS

in association with

The Spectator

First published
in book form in Great Britain in 2001 by
Profile Books Ltd
58A Hatton Garden, London EC1N 8LX
in association with
The Spectator
56 Doughty Street, London WC1N 2LL

© The Spectator, 2001

Typeset by MacGuru
info@macguru.org.uk

Printed and bound in Great Britain by
Bookmarque Ltd, Croydon, Surrey

A CIP catalogue record for this book is available from
the British Library.

ISBN 1 86197 385 3

'He always does our catering.'

BILL PROUD

'I've changed into a caring, compassionate sort of leopard.'

'Hi, I'm on the replacement bus service.'

'At least the Groundforce team didn't touch the bridge,
M'sieur Monet.'

'I see your daffs have come out, Ted.'

'Does my scum look big in this?'

'Not another record token …'

'And now a prayer for those poor souls who were damned for sins that are soft-peddled now.'

'All I'm saying is if it goes wrong again I quit!'

'He's left his body to medical research and his feet to the lucky charm factory.'

'In case you're interested, your approval rating around here
has slipped to a scant 23%.'

'This is Tarquin, my alter ego.'

'Now we can have a little chat while I'm on hold.'

The Old Lady Marcos who lived in a shoe

*'I'm afraid your snaps got mislaid
and won the Turner Prize.'*

'Now that you've all had a chance to try the shampoo,
we would like you to fill in this questionnaire.'

'Can Wolfgang come out and play?'

'We're fortunate to have a little man who comes from the village to do the gardens.'

'Yes, Jack does tend to bring his problems home from work.'

'I'll be glad when the TV's repaired.'

'How wonderful! When's it due?'

'Don't worry, I'm sure there'll be someone
along for you in a minute.'

'No, I'm sorry, you'll only go and spend it on drugs.'

BILL PROUD

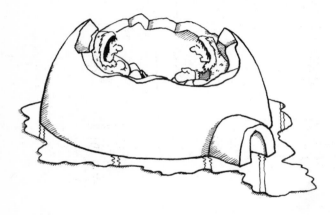

'I hate spring …'

'Iron out our differences? But surely that's women's work.'

'Misogynist? Who — me?'

'This is the largest collection of fridge-magnets
I've ever seen.'

'I'm looking for Miss Right-wing.'

'He was a door-to-door salesman.'

'Can you hear the land?'

*'It's the only thing I'm allowed to use
the hounds for these days.'*

'… and if he's naughty don't be afraid
to use the C-R-U-C-I-F-I-X …'

'Dad, can you remember when John Cleese was funny?'

BILL PROUD

'Joseph K! You have been chosen to appear on a game show!'

'Does this blood smell funny to you?'

'Grizzle, grizzle, grizzle! That's all you do! I'm sick of it!'

'To complete my minimalist decor,
there's just one more thing I need to get rid of.'

'Look at the state of you! Where's your pride?'

'Take no notice, Maria, it's the Seventh Seal.'

And so began their incredible journey …

'I hope you've left your bedroom tidy!'

'I'm on the train.'

*'I'm sorry, is this going to be a long ancient legend?
It's just that I'm double-parked.'*

'I dreamt that you died without leaving a will!'

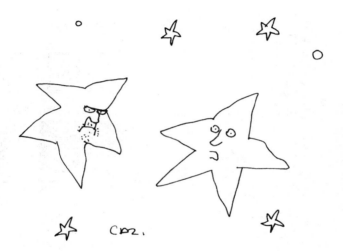

'Don't shoot — I've got a wife and four kids!'

'I need to know all the people you've been sleeping with …'

*'We're not absolutely certain.
Could you ask number five to take his hat off?'*

'Does my bum look big in this?'

'I wish you wouldn't keep nicking things from work.'

'I'm on the Stamboul Train.'

*'Parker gave an exciting presentation
followed by spontaneous combustion.
I want that kind of commitment from everyone.'*

'There was nothing on.'

'Swapping shirts is usually enough, Darren.'

*'He has to wear his brother's cast-offs.
Unfortunately, his brother's a clown.'*

'My name's Trevor and I'm the Queen of Sheba.'

'Typical men —
always bragging about whose is the smallest.'

'I think you've overdone the decking, Dave.'

'For heaven's sake, Constable!
A simple chalk outline would be sufficient!'

'Hard-boiled.'

'You're right. I was a fool to have given in to those damned animal rights activists.'

'"If she swims she's a witch; if she drowns she's innocent."
There's nothing about synchronised swimming.'

'I'm afraid he wants his ashes
trodden into your stair-carpet.'

'And which newspaper would you like
to be squashed with tomorrow morning, sir?'

'I can't come to work today. I'm in bed with a nasty bug.'

'Me just invent fire.'

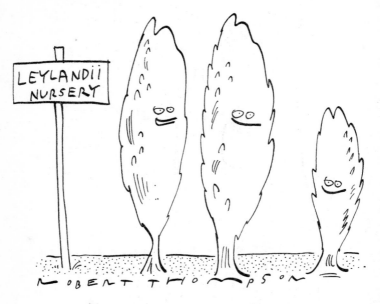

'Gosh, don't they grow up so quickly!'

'I hate this job — you do your best and all you get is flak.'

'I couldn't help it — I just sneezed ...'

'If that's work, tell them I don't exist.'

'Look, kid, the world changes.'